Dale & Sylvia Martin
Mar. 1969

# Fatigue
# in Modern
# Society

EDITED BY PAUL TOURNIER

TRANSLATED BY JAMES H. FARLEY

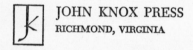

JOHN KNOX PRESS
RICHMOND, VIRGINIA

This book contains essays selected from *Surmenage et repos*, published by Éditions Delachaux & Niestlé, 1963.

Unless otherwise indicated, Scripture quotations are from the Revised Standard Version, copyright 1946 and 1952 by the Division of Christian Education of the National Council of the Churches of Christ in the United States of America.

LIBRARY OF CONGRESS CATALOG CARD NUMBER: 65-19582

© M. E. BRATCHER 1965

PRINTED IN THE UNITED STATES OF AMERICA

2726

# CONTENTS

# PREFACE
## Paul Tournier

I have long admired the considerable and remarkable work done in the United States by the Christian education departments of the various Protestant denominations. Through a systematic, well-organized, well-thought out, and widely diffused effort, they bring to the faithful a very valuable complement to the intellectual, spiritual, psychological, and social culture. They help the faithful to become aware of the great practical problems of modern life—personal, familial, and social—and to resolve these problems in the light of the Christian faith.

There is nothing in Europe comparable to this vast undertaking. But although America has organizational genius, the French often command our respect with their capacity for improvisation. In this regard, one of the most attractive of the French Protestant works is CIMADE [Comité Inter-Mouvements Auprés Des Evacués]. Thanks to the enthusiastic dedication of its pioneers, CIMADE has succeeded, with very small financial means, in bringing effective aid to countless victims of war and refugees of all nationalities and religions. Much of the credit for this success goes to Madeleine Barot.

Two young CIMADE physicians, Pierre Bernard and his wife, had the idea of organizing a Protestant Medico-Social Congress (Paris, 1948). As is well known, French

Protestants are a very small minority, yet their cultural and social level is usually superior to that of the majority of Frenchmen. They also show an active need to establish close ties among themselves. Such was especially the object of the first Congress which, from the very first, grouped not only Protestant physicians, but also the nurses and the public health workers who are called to work with the physicians in the hospitals and in the service of all the sick.

The success of Dr. Bernard's initiative has encouraged other colleagues in turn to organize analogous Congresses by bringing together some of their friends. During the past few years there have been seven Congresses, always better attended and more carefully organized. All of the meetings have come from personal initiative: Paris, 1948 (Dr. Bernard); Lyon, 1950 (Dr. W. Brunat); Bordeaux, 1951 (Dr. Ph. Kressmann); Strasbourg, 1953 (Dr. Fr. Trensz); Montpellier, 1954 (Dr. Cazalis); Paris, 1956 (Dr. Dominique Bonnet); and Evian, 1961 (Dr. Maud Cousin).

Although I am not French, my colleagues have always done me the honor of inviting me. With the exception of the Montpellier Congress, which I was prevented from attending, I have always taken a part in the meetings.

But although the initial purpose of these Congresses was to tighten the ties between Protestants who devote their professional lives to the sick, it was soon realized that these meetings could also effectively serve as a means to study the major problems of modern medicine which can be clarified by the Christian faith. Thus, for example, the Bordeaux meeting dealt with the meaning of responsibility; Strasbourg, with the relations between health and the religious life; Paris, with respect for life;

and Evian, with overwork and rest. This present book groups together some of the papers presented at Evian.

The Congresses, however, are only one aspect of the finished work. In many regions of France, work-groups are formed to prepare for the Congresses through preliminary discussions. These work-groups remind one somewhat of the Christian education departments of American churches.

The progress of medicine depends primarily on the progress of science and technology. It is clear that in this domain believers can contribute no more than can unbelievers. To be sure, they undoubtedly bring their sense of responsibility, their dedication, their professional conscientiousness, their morality. But who would dare to deny that eminent examples of these qualities are found in atheistic physicians and nurses?

The methods and disciplines of science and technology are rigidly the same for unbelievers and for believers. It is even perhaps sometimes true that the religious concerns of physicians involved in the life of the churches make of them men who are less exclusively and passionately devoted to scientific research. Perhaps their religious zeal sometimes can even constitute a psychological compensation for a certain scientific inferiority. And inversely, without their being aware of it, certain unbelieving physicians can find some compensation for the emptiness of soul which their atheism involves, such compensation coming through the almost religious fervor that they bring to scientific research. They believe in science in the same manner that we believe in the sovereignty of God, and this confidence in the progress of science gives meaning to their lives.

However, it should be pointed out that I am not setting up as opposites faith in science and faith in God, since it is God who has instituted science, who has given man the qualities proper to scientific research, and who has guided man in the great and fruitful adventure of the building of science. I am simply indicating that conscious faith in God does not play a direct role in scientific research.

But it is also clear that although scientific progress is the primary factor of medical progress, the practical efficacity of medical activity does not depend exclusively on scientific progress. The personal influence and contact of the physician with his patient also have their effects in the healing process. This is because men constantly compromise their health through their indiscretions of life, their lack of discipline, their conflicts, their errors of hygiene. Many illnesses occur neither abruptly nor by chance, but have been prepared through years of a comportment contrary to the laws of life.

An illness must always be the occasion for a taking stock of oneself, for a growing awareness of unresolved problems, and for a revision of the values which few men undertake in full health. There are resolutions to make, passions to subdue, an attitude in face of existence to change. Thus the physician, without neglecting any of his technical treatments, also has a pedagogical task: he must re-educate his patients, helping them to reform their lives.

This is especially evident in the cases of overwork and fatigue that are alluded to in this book. It is not sufficient to proceed to a clinical examination and laboratory analyses; to prescribe tonics, vitamins, rest; or to administer soporifics in an attempt to re-establish a long-compromised sleep. The patient must be helped to understand why he has arrived at his present state and what he must do to change his way of living. A state of exhaustion and fatigue is always a warning signal of the organism.

Now, although patients generally submit voluntarily to technical prescriptions and agree to take medicine or a rest-cure, they are, on the contrary, quite reticent when it comes to changing something in their way of living. This is also much more difficult. The patient even hopes sometimes that the technical medicine will assure his healing without his having to give up that which compromised his health in the first place. A frenetic activism is sometimes a compensation for some private anxiety, a flight from oneself, or the consequence of unresolved conflicts. Thus it is not sufficient to prescribe, to counsel, to exhort. It is necessary to understand profoundly the person of the patient, his evolution in life, his relationships with those around him, to help him to become more open. The physician must become friends with him, and must exercise a personal influence over him.

Thus, the physician's task is twofold: on the one side, it is scientific and technical; on the other, it is pedagogical, psychological, ethical, even spiritual. For our attitude in life is always a religious one, whether one is a believer or not: as we are toward God, so also are we toward our neighbor, toward the world, toward ourselves and life. It is in this second aspect of the physician's mission that his faith plays an eminent role. For he can help others to reform their lives only to the extent that he himself reforms his own. It is his own experience which he must communicate, the verities which he himself has tried and tested.

It is also in this domain where collaboration between

physicians, nurses, public health workers, and clergymen is especially fruitful. In the technical domain the physician is the scientist and the nurse must simply execute his decisions. But when it is a matter of the reforming of a life, the nurse can give the physician indispensable information which escapes him. This is because the nurse lives with her patient and hears his secrets. She observes his behavior, his reactions, his relationships with others.

This was all discussed at a recent meeting at a French center of treatment of tuberculosis. Present were specialists in pulmonary consumption, Roman Catholic and Protestant chaplains from various sanatariums, and nuns. While the physicians and theologians learnedly debated and wondered in which cases it would be necessary to deal with the moral problems of the patients and how to deal with them, a Dominican sister leaned over and whispered in my wife's ear: "But all the patients have problems of life which secretly torment them. That is obvious to us. To be convinced of it, all that is necessary is to listen to them a little."

Granted, the physician has little time to listen to his patients. He is especially absorbed with the scientific aspects posed by the case. As medicine makes progress, the physician will be proportionately more burdened with his technical task. But he will also need proportionately to be reminded that the healing of his patient does not depend solely on his treatments, but also on the solution of the patient's life-problems. Yet in this domain the physician is more perplexed than in the domain of science. He has his own problems, and perhaps he has encountered no one who is concerned with helping him resolve these problems. Here is where the medico-social Congresses, such as those in France, and the American Christian education groups can be useful. This is also why a hospital chaplain cannot be content with being only the chaplain to patients. He must also be chaplain to the physicians and nurses, in order that they can be led to a living experience of God which can transform their lives.

# Fatigue and Modern Life

PAUL TOURNIER

We must become more and more practical. This is not to say that we should oppose the search for the guiding ideas which the Bible gives to us. On the contrary, we wish to associate the two approaches. As Pastor Marc Boegner says, we must "search the Scriptures," but we must also probe ourselves and allow ourselves to be probed by God in the practical reality of our lives. We are concerned with modern life, but we are concerned *with ourselves* in this modern life.

Modern life is we ourselves; it is not others. Recently a patient visited me whom I had already seen four or five times during the past two years. He is one of those men who displays a profound fatigue, suffering from a neurosis whose major symptom is asthenia. He works as a steward in a large boarding school, which means that he is very busy. This institution is directed by an eminent and respected educator, who is also a man of great moral worth. Like many men of great moral worth, he is a difficult employer, very strict with himself and very demanding of his subordinates.

My patient told me that all of his predecessors had had innumerable conflicts with this employer, whereas he himself had the good fortune to get along very well with the employer, because he complied with his will without saying anything.

Well, after a length of time, I subtly began to ask him if, perhaps, this great abnegation, which he considered to be a Christian virtue and which assured him peace with his director, was not also a culpable capitulation. Of course, I proceeded very carefully. I did not want him to think that I was insinuating that his virtues could perhaps be culpable. Nevertheless, the idea took root. The other day the crisis came. And, moreover, it took him completely by surprise. When his director imposed a new demand on him, he fled. He ran away without a word, and went to the home of a friend. "You have put yourself in the wrong," said his friend. "You must return to your Institute and have the courage to explain yourself to your director!"

This is what he did. To his great astonishment, he was very well received by his director, who expressed his esteem for him. The director manifested above all his surprise: "What's the matter?" he asked. "I thought that everything was going smoothly between us."

Unfortunately, such misunderstandings happen more often than we think. My patient had the necessity of undeceiving his employer: "Things are not going as well as you think, and not only for me. But nobody dares to confront you in order to tell you what is wrong in the place."

There was a situation concerning the cook who enjoyed the favor of the director and who felt thereby that she could boss the whole show, even to the point of making personal profit, without anyone daring to say anything about it. There was a situation with the man in charge of the farms who was constantly drunk, and with whom the steward regularly lost much time uselessly. In short, there were sources of fatigue for which remedies were needed. The installation of a telephone would also have saved time for the steward, who had to go down three floors each time someone asked him for information.

Of course, the director was completely astonished. He found that there were a great number of things to change. But perhaps the most important thing is that a completely new relationship is now established between him and his steward, based on frankness, honesty, and also on the constructive principles of collaboration. The cook has left, and so has the farmer. Things cost less than before, and an interior telephone system will be installed. And, all at once, my patient is less tired, because what fatigues us most is not always normal work but that which the behavior of others adds to it.

Yes, there are often causes of fatigue which accompany poor organization. And sometimes in a business the employees have quite good ideas for improving its organization, ideas which the major executives do not think of and which no one dares mention to them.

I would also like to say a brief word to those who are in charge of clinics. I have cared for enough overburdened nurses and social welfare workers not to miss this opportunity to speak frankly and tell social welfare workers, nurses, and physicians that, when something is not working properly, it is often the fault of the directors. In this respect, it is not sufficient to grant fellow-workers a vacation. It is necessary to see if the working conditions can be changed.

We should speak here not only of our fatigue, but also

of the fatigue which we impose on others. It is not only nurses whom I have seen exhausted, but also the wives of physicians. I have cared for a great number of them, and I can say to my colleagues that even when they are very generous, even when they care for overworked patients with a self-sacrifice beyond call, it can happen that they will not see the extreme fatigue which they impose on their immediate collaborators and also perhaps on their wives. Perhaps their wives or their nurses could easily give them excellent advice on how to improve organization with a view to avoiding fatigue as much as possible.

But physicians do not have the habit of paying attention to their wives or to their nurses. They rule, and everyone obeys them readily. The halo of their dedication shelters them from criticism, for they overwork themselves. And they readily imagine, as did the director of the Institute mentioned above, that everything is going along smoothly. Well, on occasion God can speak to us through our wife or through a nurse (not always, to be sure!). But sometimes to give ear to God is to give ear to all that God can say to us through our fellow-workers and to be concerned with their person instead of utilizing them only as instruments for a noble task. There are many physicians' wives whose lives are very trying and very difficult.

I have had, only once in my life, the unenviable post of the head of a clinic, in a private clinic. A colleague asked me to replace him during his vacation. From the moment I arrived in that clinic, I saw that a permanent conflict existed between the domestic personnel (the cook and the chambermaids) and the nurses who formed a kind of Areopagus nearer to the physician, and who were a source of fatigue and exasperation for everyone. These two departments conducted a cold war. The nurses scorned the cook and found fault with her. The cook, believing herself less appreciated, less listened to by the physician, paid little attention to the instructions regarding the diets. Thus I spent my first morning at the clinic in the kitchen. I had perceived that in this clinic for nervous disorders, the patients were cared for, but no one cared for the cook. This is a gross error of judgment, because if things go better with the cook, things go better with the patients. I quickly learned this from experience.

I am interested in everything, including the kitchen, and naturally, I tasted everything that was cooked in the pots and asked for the recipes. But during this time the cook recounted her life to me, a life which had been very hard. Obviously this was the first time that she could open herself to someone. All things considered, she was one of the sick persons who had most need of the physician, yet no one thought about this. We are so often grasped by the professional outlook that we care for the people who come to consult us as patients, without seeing that others, all around us, also need us as much as our clients do.

A clinic is a business, and many problems of the physician are the problems of a head of a business, of a "small industrialist," as Armand Vincent said. It can be very advantageous to reflect, in the sight of God, on the better organization of work in the clinic. The clinic of which I have spoken is a Christian clinic, in which the physician conducted a worship service each evening. During my famous visit to the kitchen, I asked the cook if she had a favorite verse, which I could make the theme of my evening worship service. As a matter of fact, she was criticized because she never came to the service. But she told me her favorite verse, and I chose it for my evening meditation. There is no need to say that the cook was there that evening and that everyone noticed it. She was reintegrated into the community.

All of this plays a role regarding fatigue, because although fatigue often arises from organization defaults, it also quite often comes from both interior and exterior conflicts. In our own being there can be conflicts between the cook and the nurses, i.e., between the stomach and the mind.

In order to rediscover the creative imagination, in order to see the problems that are raised and that we skirt without confronting, in order to understand them, to reflect on them and to resolve them, we must know how to stop and observe a moment of contemplation. I try to guard against distinguishing between simple reflection and religious meditation; I would rather join the two. It is already a common custom to have regularly scheduled meetings to try to discover what is not going smoothly in an enterprise, be it in the office of a private physician or in a clinic. But if this could be done in the presence of God, if we could, out of faith and because we know that God is always there, turn this reflection bit by bit into meditation, then it would become even more fruitful. To meditate is to listen to God; it is also to listen to him through the mouths of our fellow-workers. Then our search takes on a new dimension, because God is able to intervene, to inspire us with solutions to all the conflicts and problems of organization, in short, to the problems of our "modern life."

Yet we need to have the inclination, the desire, and the will to make a sufficiently sizeable place in our life for meditation. I think that this is the problem which afflicts all of us. It is a problem that obsesses us constantly or in any case, the majority of us: to know that the part of our day accorded to the active life and that reserved for the meditative life are totally disproportionate. This is the case in the world of today, but it is also the case in our own life, and we have a perpetual guilty conscience in this regard. But the guilty conscience is of no use if we do not seek a solution to the problem.

This problem faced me in a particularly acute fashion about thirty years ago, in 1932. I had a very good friend, Dr. Mentha, who has since died. We spoke of the problem often then. I played a large role in the church, debating for the true theology against the bad. But I had a guilty conscience, for I was well aware that my personal piety was poverty-stricken compared to my ecclesiastical activity. At that time Mentha, who was a practical man, said to me that we should discuss it with one of our minister friends. This friend has since become a professor of theology. Mentha went to see him, and told him: "You theologians sail in the clouds. You must see what our life is in reality. Yesterday I was awakened by the telephone, and had to make an urgent visit. I ran to that place, and when I returned two people awaited me, and while I was treating them, another urgent telephone call came . . . In short, you know what a physician can encounter in his daily activity. Well, then, where would you like us to include a time for meditation?"

This pastor was an honest man, and replied to him: "Yes, I understand. It is very difficult! Let me think about it, and we will speak of it again."

He thought about it so well that many events passed in the meantime. One evening, during a meeting with some friends that had been organized by Mentha, I heard a Dutchman speak of the importance that meditation played in his life. After our discussions were over, I went straight to question him: "Tell me, sir, how much time do you devote each day to your meditation?" He was a very active man, burdened with many responsibilities, a high official in the League of Nations. This was not a dreamer lost in the clouds.

"That depends," he replied quietly.

"No!" I replied heatedly. "Answer me exactly! How much time do you set aside?"

"At least a half-hour," he said. "Normally an hour, often enough, two."

I returned home, and the next day I arose an hour earlier, trying not to awaken my wife, for I would have been a bit ashamed were she to ask, "What are you doing?" I went into my office, put my watch before me, and said to myself: I want very much to see what will come from an hour of meditation. From time to time I looked at my watch, in order to be quite certain to keep my promise.

I was well enough educated to trace out in my head at least twenty sermons on a biblical passage that I had just recently read. I was quite accustomed to working with ideas on God. But I felt that that was not the question, that it was a question of something completely different, that it was a question of encountering God and not of exposing ideas about God. I spent there an hour of terrible humiliation. I thought that many men who had nothing of my religious activity knew how to encounter God, while I knew nothing of it. I finished the hour without having the impression that God had said anything to me. Nevertheless, at the end, a thought came to me: "Continue . . . continue . . ." And I told myself, "Wait a minute! Perhaps that idea comes from God." It did not occur to me then that during that time my life had been mastered by God. I mean, to be sure, my life in its external form. I am not speaking of salvation, which is already accomplished in Jesus Christ. It is rather a question of the transformation of my life, of my relationships with everyone—with myself, my wife, my children, and my patients—which had changed. Well, all the ensuing development of my existence came out of this face-to-face encounter with God. My intimacy with him was accentuated bit by bit; my life became enriched, freed from many hindrances; it gave me a vital interest in that other side of life, for its inner dimension, so necessary to us.

But it was necessary for me to pass through that terrible embarrassment which I had met there, that embarrassment which scholars or religious people can know when they truly try to make a clean sweep of all the religious knowledge acquired and become for them somewhat of a comfortable pedestal, of all that which gives them the flattering impression of being men of God, when they have not yet encountered him.

To encounter God is truly to put one's life faithfully under his eyes. "What does God think of my life? What does God think of my life? . . ." How many times do we put this question to ourselves, seriously and profoundly? "What does God think of my activity, of my work, of the way I organize it, of the apportionment I make of everything? What does he think of this life where there is no longer, so to speak, a place for meditation?"

My first word to my friend Mentha, after this experience, was: "You know, it works!" And Mentha, in turn, went to see the pastor again, and said to him: "We no longer have any need for you to reflect on our question, because we have made a place for meditation in our life." Mentha and I had an enormous amount of things to change in our lives. There are undoubtedly many other things remaining to be changed, but, nevertheless, the little that I have experimented with this permits me to say that a man who meditates, who tries to place his life under the attention of God, finds a life infinitely more fruitful, infinitely more harmonious, much less fatiguing and more profound.

For to live is to choose. To be a believer is to choose that which God wishes. To be a Christian is to count not only on the law to know the will of God, but also on the Holy Spirit, on the living communion with Jesus Christ. It is to live this choice; to live this search for the choice which is indispensable for putting our life in order under the direction of the Holy Spirit. For under the inspiration of God we are better able to distinguish the essential from the secondary. We eliminate many activities that are fatiguing and in no way indispensable. This is the planning of life. As we all know, much is said in our age concerning planning. Men seek blueprints inspired by reason; we must show that there is a planning of God, and we can show this only in our own lives.

"Go from your country . . ." This word of God to Abraham means: leave your habits, leave your routines, leave all which determines your life and keeps it prisoner, leave all which seemed to you to be the normal environment because you have been raised in it, because you have been instructed in it. You have been instructed by the world; leave this world, obey God, truly seek an inspiration, construct your life by an interior inspiration and not according to the contagion of the world which has too great a hold over you.

This is what is at stake in each of our days, in each of our decisions. This is the great remedy for an evil from which we all suffer: dissipation of efforts. Men are in a hurry, and we physicians and pastors even more so than others. We have too many irons in the fire. Therein lies an important distinction which we can make in the light of the Bible: the distinction between "toil" and "work." When the Bible speaks of the toil of God, it speaks of his work. This word evokes something coherent, something that can be fulfilled, something that has an internal unity. The more life is guided by God, the more it frees itself from fragmented toil in order to acquire, little by little, the character of a work.

For this it is necessary to choose, to sacrifice a great many things. It is not necessary only to do what appears to be good, useful, or noble, but rather to do that which God wants. Remember David, when God kept him from building the Temple! It is a fine undertaking to want to build a temple for God, but to construct it when God does not want it, and when it is not God's chosen time, is time wasted. It is disobedience, not obedience. How many well-intentioned disobediences do our lives contain? That is the problem!

Sometimes the inspiration of God can be very practical. It is not only a matter of finding certain major directive lines which make of our life a work, but also of resolving the very smallest concrete questions of each day, especially those questions which give rise to fatigue.

Each instance of fatigue is a signal. Each instance of fatigue calls us to meditate a little more, for it can be the sign that something is not in order in our life, something which we must examine before God. The question has previously been raised, "What are the fatigues of obedience and what are the fatigues of disobedience?" The theologian has rightly replied that an all-inclusive formula cannot be given. Each individual at each instant, each time he is tired, must see if God has something to say to him through this fatigue. That is the answer, to be attentive to God, to seek constantly what God has to say to us. Thus Elijah, fatigued to the point of desiring death, went to the desert, because he still had something to learn from God. There he heard the "still, small voice," that small voice of meditation in which God revealed to him that he is not only in the great "free-for-alls" which Elijah had supported so courageously, but that he is also in a tender love. Soon, God gave him a fellow-worker in the person of Elisha.

At the beginning of the war, in 1939, a friend whom I had previously treated came to my office. Arnold Müggli was one of those puny men who always appear to be at the end of their strength, often ill, and to whom physicians are compelled to recommend that they live very restricted lives. Now, the Swiss Federal Government had asked him to take charge of food-rationing for the country during the war. It can easily be understood that this was a task which would not permit him to live a restricted existence (moreover, this fact was later confirmed when we were surrounded by the German armies and their allies, and would have been at their mercy had we not had something to eat).

So Arnold Müggli asked me, "How should I reply?"

My response was, "If you die in the job, you will not be the first one to have given his life for his country." But I added, "I do not think that God wishes your death, but more probably a new experience of life; perhaps he will give you some practical indications for assuming such a heavy task without dying from it." And we fell silent, together, before God.

My friend, afterward, read to me what he had written in his notebook during that moment of silence: "I will not live at Berne; I will leave my family at Zürich; I will go to Berne from Monday morning to Friday evening, in order to be able to give myself to my work without being split between it and my family . . . [this is often a cause of fatigue; such a division between several duties impedes concentration] on Friday evening I will return home to Zürich in order to devote all of Saturday to reflecting tranquilly on the major problems which one never has the time to think about when one is pestered by the telephone in the office . . . [this is also a frequent cause of fatigue, this lack of time to reflect on essentials because one is taken up with incidentals] finally, on Sunday, I will cease to work, and I will give myself entirely to my family." This is what he did, and he assumed his task with so much authority and wisdom that the University of Zürich named him Doctor of Medicine *Honoris causa*. And at the end of the war he was in infinitely better health than before.

Yes, God can inspire us with organizational measures which we would not have had by ourselves and which prove to be very sensible. God can also show us on whom to unload certain of our tasks instead of assuming

them all by ourselves. There is a well-known passage in
the Bible (Exod. 18:13-27) where Jethro, Moses' father-
in-law, tells Moses, in sum, "You're going to be bushed,
done in, if you continue like that! You absolutely must
commit some of your work to others."

I imagine that it was Moses' wife who had become
well aware that her husband was tiring himself out, but
in those times the wife was less emancipated than today,
so Zipporah instructed her father to mention it to her
husband. But even today a woman does not always make
her husband understand such a salutary caution. In any
event, Moses listened to God: he heard the voice of divine wisdom which was expressed through his father-in-
law and he was able to name judges to act as his depu-
ties. Everyone has the problem of knowing how to
unburden himself, for everyone is possessive, especially
those, perhaps, who do not think they are. Each person
wants to fulfill his tasks by himself, from the great man at
the summit of the hierarchy to the nurse who does not
tolerate someone else meddling in "her" ward.

We can see that Moses profited from the lesson, because later, when he had to keep his arms upraised in
order for the people to gain the victory, he accepted the
aid of Aaron and Hur, one on each side, in supporting
his tired arms. This is a beautiful image for our subject:
to accept assistance. But nothing is more difficult than for
an active man to accept assistance. He barricades himself and isolates himself. If someone wants to remove
some of his burden, he immediately feels that there is a
plot to dethrone him, that he is about to "get the ax."

Meditation and this search for a sovereignty of God in
the organization of our lives is the remedy for hurry and

commotion. We see this perfectly in Jesus. How much greater than any of ours was Jesus' responsibility—the responsibility of saving the world! If there was ever on this earth a being who could be tempted to bustle about, to hurry everywhere, to want to see everyone in order to fulfill his task, it was Jesus Christ. But what do we see? That wondrous calm that shines forth in the Gospels. Jesus had time to speak tranquilly with a woman whom he met at the well. They brought him children, and the disciples rushed forward: do not disturb the Master with these children. But no, he had time for children, he had time for those who came to him. And his great mission, his mission for all the entire world, was fulfilled in that total giving of himself to each person, in that calm and completely personal dialogue with each one. This example has a vital import for us.

The yield of our life does not depend so much on the number of things that we do, but more on the quality of self-giving that we put to each thing. In order to add this quality, we must depart from this atmosphere of the modern world which is completely obsessed with activism, even in the church: do, do, do always more. Let us rather, once again, become inspired and tranquil men.

Fatigue also comes from the internal divisions of our own being, the rebellions, the unresolved problems of life that can be resolved in meditation. Just the other day I received a letter from a nurse: "You are going to give a speech on modern life and its fatigue; what fatigues me is to return home in the evening after a day of full blossoming and find myself completely alone in my home." I know what this fatigue is, this fatigue of the unmarried person's solitude. I also know that this fatigue, linked to

woman's every instinct and of every need for tenderness
revolting against her unmarried situation, is a problem
which cannot be resolved through a frenzy of outside activity, no matter how pleasant it might be. It can be resolved only in meditation. In this regard I recalled the
word of Naomi to Ruth, when she told her to remarry in
order to find "repose in marriage." To be sure, it can be
somewhat dangerous to consider marriage as a repose.
Nevertheless, the Bible says it. There is, indeed, a repose
in not being alone. And if one is alone through the single
life, there is only one means of being no longer alone, and
that is to be with God.

To rediscover our inner unity! This inner unity, which
is so necessary to a true radiance, and an efficacious action, is created in meditation. Many times in seeking in
meditation the hidden causes of our fatigues, we discover
what still divides us, and we are then able to receive
from God a more harmonious inner unity and what I
would call a spirit of repose which can rule not only in
our moments of repose but also in full activity.

Everyone knows this word of Habakkuk: "the nations
weary themselves for naught" (2:13). For naught! Men
of today speak much of this. Indeed, that is what fatigues, to work for naught, because one has forgotten that
the condition for effectiveness is to be in contact with
God. A man in contact with God adjusts his life to his
temperament. There are very diverse temperaments, as
everyone knows. My temperament is completely different from that of Jean-Pierre Vernes or André Sarradon.
I have an inclination toward tranquility; they are in-
clined toward activity. God knows this quite well, and it
is he who has created us so different. He can thus use

each of us according to our temperament if he leads us. Thus, there is a diversity of temperaments and the same obedience.

I would like to address a few words to women. The woman obviously has more of an appreciation for the person than the man does. More than man, she has an appreciation for life-in-depth. If she lets herself go too far with her modern emancipation, to the point of giving primacy in her life to "doing" over "being," she will be thrown into an inner conflict. It will be a conflict between that which she truly is and that which she becomes through the inducement of modern life. It will be a conflict between her need to live in the order of "being" and all that which urges her to live in that of "doing."

Yet the most important thing in meditation is not those practical inspirations that we can receive to organize our life more satisfactorily. These are valuable, as I have just emphasized. But the true meaning of meditation is to deepen our intimacy with God; it is to learn to live in constant communion with Jesus Christ, to share everything with him. To seek our path each day with him is above all to learn to know him and to make him really a party to our life.

Recall the beginning of Calvin's catechism: "What is the end of man?" The end of man is to know God, and man's happiness is also to know God.

We could testify to concrete experiences received in meditation, which have enriched our life. But whatever these experiences be, they still remain quite precarious, incomplete, hesitant. What counts most is that in seeking thus to put our life under the light of God, it is God himself who takes an increasingly greater place in our life. It is no longer simply the God of Sunday. It is our entire professional life that we live with him. Then each patient seems sent by him; regarding each one, we come closer to Jesus Christ, and we ask him: "What thinkest thou of this?" We seek his aid, his light, his blessing for our daily work, even for the most technical work.

I assure you that there are then no more "bores." No, one is interested in everyone, because God is passionately interested in everyone. And this interest involves a new experience of God in reference to each person and each professional act because each time we learn to know God more fully. Even more, it involves a new experience of God in reference to all acts of life, to all the events of family life, during vacation and recreation times as well as during work, for the meaning of life is to do everything with God.

However, I am convinced that it is very difficult to meditate. Despite what I have said, I must confess that it often happens that I have to cut short my meditation or even to postpone it. Or sometimes we only pretend to meditate, in order to keep our promise. But a true spirit of meditation, a true desire to find God, is missing. It is because of these infidelities that we have had qualms about speaking of meditation. We have prudently avoided giving testimonies, because we realize that they are too often contradicted by our behavior. There is also an element of a conspiracy of silence: we scarcely dare to speak of the value of meditation for fear that someone will ask, "Do you meditate as faithfully as you exhort us to do? Did you meditate well this morning?" But it would also be treason, because of our unfaithfulness, to keep silent about the victories we have gained, the positive experiences that we have had and which mark the most decisive hours of our life.

Can we not quite simply proclaim both our conviction of the incomparable value of meditation and confess that we too frequently miss the mark in this respect? I often practice written meditation. This has the great advantage of making the meditation more precise, of conserving the text of it, of my being more constrained to follow the inspirations that come from it. It also has the advantage of conserving the date in one's notebook. Just recently I spent two weeks of vacation during which time I was very pressed for time, because I wanted to write two small books. On returning home from my vacation, I opened my notebook and saw that the last date entered was on the eve of my departure. If there is any time when we should find a lot of time for meditation, it is during vacations. I was extremely humiliated!

I also realized immediately that I should confess this to a patient who shortly before had begun to take his first steps in meditation. He had asked many questions on the subject and had indicated an interest in my experiences. Well, I summoned up my courage and told him about the two dates in my notebook. He then told me that I had helped him more by my confession than by everything I had told him previously. We can help people through the witness of our positive experience, but we also help them by our frankness in telling them about our difficulties and failures.

Now, there remains a major difficulty to be mentioned here: how do we know the will of God? How do we know what he wants us to change in our lives? How do we know what he wants us to do and what he wants us

not to do? This is not easy, and I think that the most
sincere Christians often deceive themselves in this respect. Jesus himself hesitated several times. There is a
passage in the Bible where Jesus invited his disciples to
withdraw from the crowd, because the crowd pressed
them to the point where they had no time to eat. But on
the other side of the lake they found the crowd once
again, where it had rushed. Then, instead of fleeing even
further, Jesus changed his mind. He spoke to the crowd,
and even stayed to feed them (the multiplication of the
loaves).

In the same way, when the Canaanite woman came
to Jesus, he refused her by invoking the plan of God
which intended that he not spread out his efforts but that
he rather devote himself to the people of Israel. We also
should learn to say no sometimes to quite legitimate requests, through obedience to God. But when the Canaanite woman declared her well-known confession of
faith, Jesus changed his mind and gave her what she
asked. To meditate, to seek the will of God, is not to
know securely what this will is. Far from it! It is to grope
for it in darkness, to be often mistaken, sometimes even
to remain for long periods with no response to our press-
ing questions. It is to run a risk, but it is to persevere ob-
stinately, despite all difficulties, for it is more important
to seek than to find.

In spite of all these hesitations, meditation remains the
source of every great reform of life. This is true for ourselves, and it is true also for our patients. Medicine is not
only a thing of prescribing medicines, penicillin, placen-
tary extracts, or paid vacations. It is not with technical
means alone that we are able to heal sick people. Medi-

cine is also a matter of reforming lives, to help patients to abandon their poor way of life which compromises their physical and moral health. The profound meaning of medicine, aside from all the adjuvants which we can use, is to aid sick people to put their lives in order, to rediscover the order of God. This is basic. It is more effective, in many cases, than a whole arsenal of therapeutics (which, of course, I do not reject).

For this it is necessary for men to learn to meditate, to return home to themselves. It is not a matter of teaching them a given technique of meditation, but to initiate them into an ineluctable verity, to know that the exterior life depends on the inner life, that every reform of life presupposes an intimate evolution, and if this profound renewal is missing, then all the resolutions and all the good advice remain quite insufficient. Counsel an overworked executive, tell him to rest—you will see how difficult it is to get him to do it. Perhaps he will rest if you prescribe a visit to the spa at Evian. Such a thing would be good, but his life would not yet be transformed, and after returning from his vacation, he would simply begin again to overwork. Lead him to find God, and the whole climate of his existence will change. Moreover, perhaps it will be at Evian, because of this salutary arrest of his frenetic life, that he will encounter God; then his rest cure will have a completely different import.

But how can we reform the life of our patients if our own is not? Any physician knows that patients are not deceived. "Physician, heal thyself!" Our patients know us better than we realize. They know very well when we prescribe for them relaxation that we do not practice ourselves. There are even ministers who speak wondrously of peace, yet one feels that they do not have it.

It is one thing to distinguish the evil, to see that it is necessary to change, that it is necessary to rediscover a deep tranquility, and another thing to truly reform one's life, to enter into practical obedience, to make this program a reality in our actions. For this, a superior strength is necessary, the strength of God. For the price is often considerable.

It is very hard to cut one's life off from many interesting things, to refuse to perform many useful services. But it is a question not only of our life, but of our witness to the world. We should rediscover a prophetic attitude vis-à-vis the modern world. Yes, this modern world, this hustle and bustle, this universal fatigue, all has the meaning of a judgment of God. It is like the fulfillment of innumerable pages of the Bible: if you turn away from God, your works will be in vain, you will exhaust yourself for nothing. This is what we see before our eyes. It is necessary to proclaim this to the world and to show in our own life that there is a solution. Our fatigue is above all the sign of an estrangement from God and the great fatigue of the modern world expresses its immense need of rediscovering God. We are in a situation analogous to that of the people of Israel after the golden calf: this people is completely disoriented. It has need of rediscovering a direction. Then God said to it: "My presence will go with you, and I will give you rest" (Exod. 33:14).

This prophetic position should be taken by physicians, nurses, and social welfare workers as well as by theologians. It is in this perspective that all our personal experiences find their meaning, in that of a witness. What is the meaning of the Christian life?—to render witness to

Jesus Christ. Pastors must render witness through the ministry of the word, and we laymen must witness through our lives. Modern life is ourselves, our present life; to render witness to Jesus Christ is to show what he can do. We have allowed ourselves to be contaminated by the world, seized by inner conflicts by dint of running after all the gods of the modern world; we have submitted to the ascendancy of the world, that of restlessness and of fear. As Christians we should, in the presence of God, take a step backward and look at ourselves, in order to examine ourselves sternly, in order to be able then to speak to the world with authority and to bring it a response.

And that brings me to my last word: modern life has only begun. Today's restlessness is only a stammering compared to what it promises to be in a century. Therefore, do not long for the good old days, for the bygone days of the coach-and-four and the liveried footmen, when one had leisure time, but when the time of some was paid for by the slavery to work of the majority. Let us rather look ahead to see how technical progress can serve humanity. It seems that we know only how to create bitter men, who reject their time and who know only how to complain. The world is in process of transformation; a mutation infinitely greater than we can imagine is taking place before our eyes. Let us open our eyes and try to understand what is happening. You should read books like that of Louis Armand: *Plaidoyer pour l'avenir (Plea for the Future)*. They show us that the world is at the threshold of an extraordinary transformation in which, all at once, finally, abundance will exist, and abundance which recalls that proclaimed by God to his people when he spoke of the country flowing with milk and honey. We are soon going to find ourselves confronted by a world that we do not recognize and before which even the most venturesome technicians will continue to marvel. With abundance, leisure time will come for everyone; what will men do with it? Will the church think far enough ahead, with enough freshness, to be able to understand it, to make provision for it and respond to it, to conduct its people to God and bring God back to the center of this new world? That is the problem of modern life.

Everyone knows the advice of those who have been financially successful: "Rack your brain!" Today businessmen are racking their brains. Will the church be able to rack its brain? Will it be able to take an interest in the future, to seek God's solutions for new problems, solutions which do not oppress the individual in the mass, but which will integrate him, as a person, into a living and inspired community? Will the church become "prospective"?

It is the church which should ask itself why God has given to man the intelligence and the scientific knowledge which have permitted him to master atomic power. There is a plan of God, there is a hidden intention of God, in all new evolution, and it is the church which must seek them out and reveal them. It must teach man what use he should make of the powers that God has given to him. All comes from God. All is a gift from God. All must serve the plan of God. In our own life and in the world, we are called to seek how God intends us to use all that which he has given to us.

# The Treatment of Fatigue

ANDRÉ SARRADON

I would simply like to make some *critical reflections* on the use of medicines, placing myself, moreover, in a very general point of view and in a very broad perspective.

The treatment of fatigue is essential. But it has often been studied from a strictly utilitarian point of view as the by-product of work.

Our experience as practitioners reveals to us that there is a considerable disproportion between the causes of fatigue and its effects on the familial and social level. We have all noticed that in the number of divorces, of difficulties in parent-children relationships, or of social relationships, it is often the small surface ripples and nervous diatheses that are more poisonous than the great storms of passion.

On the other hand, fatigue leads to a diminution of the strength of the self, which makes possible the dissolution of our capacities to maintain a coherence of the personality, and opens the door to passivity in face of the rising of impulses.

Although religion and ethics have the mission of fixing the goals of our conduct, the humane sciences (and medicine in particular) can perhaps help man to attain these goals, by providing the means to do so.

The prophylactic preventative treatment of fatigue consists of avoiding the causes of fatigue, through the organization of work, the techniques of relaxation during work, etc. I will dwell only briefly on this subject.

I would like to emphasize once more *the primacy of the ensemble of emotional reactions* whenever human behavior is involved. Someone who is happy, who is satisfied in his life and in his activity, is untireable, but the worst "plugger" cracks like a disjointed puppet if he receives an emotional traumatism or if he no longer has that existential satisfaction coming from fulfilling oneself through forming an integral part of a greater whole.

The second way of avoiding fatigue is *training*. I will not tarry on this subject, even though it is the most valuable solution. Indeed, whether it involves the athlete, the intellectual, or the laborer, training represents a form of physiological adjustment for increasing yield and performance without leading to fatigue. Training thus permits the suppression of fatigue, while at the same time preserving this need for personal fulfillment and for the vital expansion which characterizes the contemporary man (as well as man in general).

But I want to pass over that in order to deal with curative treatment. I will also jump very rapidly over the *nonmedical* treatments. Much has been said concerning proper nutrition, sleep, hydrotherapy, and the style of life.

Let us observe, simply, that if it is difficult to make someone work who does not want to, it is even more difficult to hinder someone from working who wants to, who is obsessed by his activity. Westerners should meditate more on this Laotian proverb: "If you are in the mood to work, go to bed, and it will pass."

We will look at medicinal treatment first in its basic principle. It has three ends: energizing recuperation, the regulation of neurohormonal systems, and the suppression of subjective discords.

*Energizing recuperation.* Briefly, this is the utilization of all the well-known products: the beloved calcium; phosphoric acid or the amino acids; the whole alphabet of vitamins A, B, C, D, with their coefficients 2, 3, 4, 5, 6, 12, etc.; together with their always-inflated dosage. What is happening in this domain is somewhat similar to the situation with respect to automotive fuels, where the battle of super-extra and extra-super is well known. We have vitamin C 100, C 500, C 1000—who knows where it will end? All types of cocktails are allowed, and it would seem that they are not deleterious. But in reality, they are only therapies for vitamin deficiency and could not begin to warrant this enormous consumption of vitamins.

The second point is perhaps more important and more difficult. This is *the regulation of neurohormonal systems* which regulates adjustment and a return to a normal homeostasis.

It is certain that many physiological studies are presently centered on these problems and would seem to hold much promise for the future. We have already acquired extremely precise information, in particular, on the corticoids, on products made from thyroid extracts, and on hormonal by-products of the gonads. But it should be pointed out that, on the one hand, they are difficult to use and that, on the other hand, at least as concerns fatigue, they have not fulfilled the hopes that were placed in them on the basis of our physiological knowledge. When the physiology of fatigue is studied under the perspective of cortisone and its derivatives, or of thyroid extracts, for example, one would expect a given effect. And yet, if it is given in small doses, there is sometimes a minor improvement, but it is quite negligible. This is one type of disparity that can exist between our theoretical knowledge and the practical, clinical application of our knowledge.

Finally, the third point in the treatment of fatigue consists in *modifying subjective states*, that is, the feelings of depression and of anxiety and the alterations of temperament.

We all know that our patients come to us and say, "I'm having a nervous breakdown" (it has become fashionable), and ask for stimulants which will increase their drive and will give them, at the same time, euphoria.

At the other extreme, irritability, a nervous temperament, general hyperexcitability, and anxiety lead to the utilization of depressants, tranquilizers, and sedatives. We should point out, moreover, that there is an internal contradiction, of sorts, in the alternate use of a stimulant and a depressant, and that such a utilization is very often quite tricky.

Among my patients there is a man who takes six tablets (1.5 gr.) of Gardenal each evening and six tablets of Maxiton each morning. He came to this solution after a frantic attempt to regain his normal tempo of living, for during the day he was completely washed-out and during the night he kept everyone from sleeping. This shows how difficult it is to utilize these psycho-pharmacological products.

We would now like to say something about the dangers of utilizing drugs, from the standpoint of pharmacology. This danger arises from a certain number of *errors of utilization.*

*The first error* is that of indication. It is incontestable that there is a certain overuse of drugs.

Many cases of fatigue have nothing in common with depression in the psychiatric sense of the term, and it is as useless and dangerous for the physician to prescribe Imipramine in such cases as it is to prescribe electric shock therapy. In the same way, cases of both fatigue and of depression should not be confused with cases of serious anxiety in psychiatric patients simply because all of these types of cases manifest inquietude or emotivity (thus, of course, massive doses of Levomepromazine are entirely uncalled for in cases of serious anxiety). The same is true in endocrinology: in this field there is a disparity between the remarkable efficacity of products and the difficulty we encounter in discovering exactly how these hormonal secretions operate physiologically.

Because of this material difficulty, resulting from costly and complex techniques, we are often reduced to prescribing hormones on the basis of a hypothesis rather than on an accurate knowledge of posological certainties. This gives rise to all the disappointments and all the dangers that are encountered.

When one has gained the fearful power of transforming a perfect specimen of manhood or womanhood into an hermaphroditic aberration, it is necessary to be careful with our prescriptions.

*The second error* involves dosage. It should be recognized that all these drugs have first of all been tested on psychiatric patients. It has been only recently that this usage has been enlarged to include "normal" (so to speak) patients, and this has given rise to abuses of dosage. Everyone is now accustomed to seeing patients up and walking around after having taken Largactyl, Phenergan, etc.

This also involves the matter of the schedule of doses. It is incontestable that the dangers in the use of these drugs arise when the doses are given in too close intervals. It is wise to prescribe small doses and to spread them throughout the course of the day; the purpose of these small doses is to slow down and balance, without affecting one's alertness.

There is also a proper way to start a treatment. It should be *progressive*, on the one hand, because it would seem that there is a necessity for the body to become accustomed to drugs. If it receives drugs in excessive initial doses, it rejects them, as it were. On the other hand, gradual doses permit the physician to probe individual sensitivities.

Something should be said, moreover, concerning the danger of medication in respect to the receptability of the individual. All people have sensitivity, in varying degrees, to remedies, but it is in the field of psychopharmacology that the most astonishing variations between individual sensitivities are found. It is well known that some people become completely groggy from ¼ or ½ tablet of a depressant, while for others two tablets are needed to have sedative effect.

Moreover, this shows us that we must react (regarding fatigue as with all illnesses) against this present-day tendency to have *prefabricated therapeutic schemes* which fit everyone without differentiation.

Finally, some medicines have paradoxical reactions. We know some people who must drink a cup of coffee to be able to go to sleep, and it is not rare to find people who are stimulated by Largactyl and Phenergan.

In regard to age, children proportionately tolerate these medicines better than adults, and how many babies are stuffed with Phenergan before finally arriving at the calm sought by the family!

Physicians have not observed any major adverse reactions during lactation. It seems that we will have to forget the idea of calming the baby by giving tranquilizers to the mother in hopes that they will pass to the baby through the milk. But during pregnancy, on the contrary, it is different. Nothing much needs to be said about this, since the front pages of the newspapers are full of the exploits of these medicines.

Everyone is acquainted with the drama of the German tranquilizer [Thalidomide]. The world presently contains thousands of deformed children (I no longer recall the numbers, but it is somewhere between 3,000 and 10,000).

We are quite aware that this was a costly drama, but if it will make patients and physicians more prudent in their enthusiasm, then perhaps the cost of this terrible and distressing experience will not be too dear.

These special cases will suffice. I will not discuss the *intolerances* which are valid for all drugs and remedies. Let us simply emphasize once again the dangers of therapy: one wonders if we are not in the process of creating a new race, "the *homo-allergicus*" of the 20th century.

Besides these critical remarks on errors arising in indications, doses, and receptability, we must consider the nondesired effects of remedies which are called side effects.

I will give only two examples: the neurocirculatory asthenia which brings on black-outs and tendencies toward fainting spells. Now, some of these drugs are circulatory depressants, or in any case they act as such to increase this neurocirculatory asthenia. As a result, the person who takes them always feels on the verge of fainting and sees his anguish increase. Thus one gives drugs to counter anxiety, and the side-effects of the remedy are more injurious, creating and increasing anguish.

The same thing happens regarding the feeling of depersonalization experienced by patients taking these drugs. This feeling increases their anguish. They resist this "chemical binding," and react by an attitude of resistance to therapy and of exaggerated anguish.

There are also *secondary reactions* ("reactions of compensation"), but I will not discuss these in order to devote attention to secondary effects which last over longer periods of time.

As is well known, certain drugs frequently have an extrapyramidal syndrome which follows their ingestion over prolonged periods. (And here I should point out that there is a new perspective in our therapeutic practices. This relatively recent development is *prolonged treatment*, "long-playing" as it were, which obliges us to rethink the problem.)

In effect, when a very toxic and very risky treatment is administered over 15 or 20 days, one is able to find out what is happening and eventually to stop. But in these new anticoagulant or anticholesterol therapies (and all the rest) which are so much in fashion, we have no idea what will be the end result after several years. And even though it is not a tranquilizer, I remind you of the history of MER 29. This was an anticholesterol product that was launched on the market with an amplitude possible only to big business. This drug is no longer in circulation. I point this out because its withdrawal was made with less noise than its arrival. It was noticed that over a long period of time, after three or four years, Americans who had undergone preventative treatment in respect to cholesterol suffered from opacity of the eye-lens, loss of hair, and premature aging. What a beautiful result, when the primary purpose was to take precautions against the hypothetical results of hypercholesterolemia.

Some of my colleagues said that they were advised of this. But it is obvious that the appropriate governmental agencies could be asked to advise physicians personally of the withdrawal of a dangerous medicine. This would necessitate about ten percent of the effort made to make the product known to physicians.

In any case, this incident can teach us a lesson, and it leads us to reflect on the unknown factor present in all pharmaceutical prescription. We know what the medicine acts upon, but there are sectors in which we do not know the effect of the medicine. This zone of incertitude and lack of knowledge must be considered and borne in mind constantly.

But in these psycho-pharmacological drugs there is a somewhat particular perspective which concerns dangers that are as human as they are specifically medical. These medicines *modify behavior,* sometimes superficially, but also sometimes in a profound way. Let us take the example of the automobile driver: if he finds himself a bit tired, he is afraid of going to sleep at the wheel. If, shortly before taking the wheel, he takes a psychotropic drug or a stimulant, in a few minutes he feels full of euphoria and dynamism. He thinks he is the champion of the Indianapolis "500" and takes the curves on two wheels, passing cars that are passing other cars. The instinct of self-preservation is practically neutralized. He flies along, the air is pure, the road is wide. But the obstacles are always there.

The inverse is true. If he is a bit nervous or excited, if he mistrusts his reflexes, he takes a tranquilizer. Then the danger, and I think a great one, is that he will fall asleep at the wheel. But the opposite phenomenon can also occur, such as recently happened to my wife (causing no little terror). She described the incident to me in detail. A remarkable and complete state of indifference is produced in the face of danger. The driver sees, with admirable serenity, the trees and the big trucks and considers them with an air of superior detachment. He has absolutely no desire to apply the brakes or to turn the wheel. My wife returned five minutes later because she told me, "I had the feeling that I would be 'carried back in something' because of my state of indifference."

There is a suppression of the most elementary instinct of self-preservation, and this shows the concrete and practical dangers.

Many examples could be given. For instance, there was the case of the venerable department head who had given twenty-five years of faithful and loyal service. He had a staff of twenty charming secretaries, and his attitude had always been irreproachable. One day he came to me and said, "Doctor, I don't know what is happening. I'll go crazy. Something is wrong with my mind. *Do* something!"

He explained that for some unknown reason, and despite himself, he had allowed himself to be moved by the curvatures of a neck or of an arm, and that he had behaved in a way that simply stupefied him. He had taken a "tonic" which a friend had given him.

Recently, also, a very attractive young couple came to me in tears. The wife had just been driven out by her father-in-law, because he thought she was completely drunk. This unfortunate woman had, indeed, taken a small drink of *pastis* [aniseed apéritif] and, shortly before, a tranquilizer. This was the first time and she was completely gaga. Actually, the odor of the anisette and her attitude had completely deceived the unfortunate father-in-law. I needed a great deal of eloquence and persuasion to make him admit that it was not a matter of inveterate alcoholism but simply of an abnormal therapeutic effect.

All of these drugs which profoundly modify the human personality should be handled with great prudence. "A restless Socrates is worth more than a satisfied pig." Human anxiety, to a certain degree, is a respectable thing.

After these remarks on the pharmacodynamic plane, I will come to the heart of the matter, approaching the subject on a psychological level. I will deal first with the patient-medicine relationship, then with the physician-medicine relationship.

*The patient-medicine relationship.* The patient comes to his physician in the expectation of a prescription more or less loaded with medicine. Some are eager for drugs, while others are more circumspect. But few people could understand it if they left a medical consultation without some sort of program or medicinal menu to follow. There is a pharmaceutical appetite, founded on therapeutic hope. A merchant of beauty products said, "We don't sell Lanolin, we sell hope!" Is this not true in the medical domain?

The "placebo" effect of medicines (their effects beyond their pharmacodynamic action) has been seriously studied. There are "placebo-positive" subjects who react favorably to these medicines without special action. There are also "placebo-negative" subjects who react in the inverse direction. With these subjects, the effect perhaps wears off quickly, or perhaps it varies according to taste, color, or mode of dispensing the medicine. Sometimes, also, bitter-tasting pills have a clearly more active "placebo" effect than sugared pills. And so on.

In our age the "placebo" effect is greatly increased by cultural influences. Publicity, directions for use, the many medical articles which litter the women's and family magazines and sports magazines, as well as politics, all result in sensitizing the subject. And scientific explications have suggestive effects which reinforce the "placebo" effects of medicines.

Likewise, the confidence of the patient in his physician is also basic. The good relationship makes the medicine felt as a "good object," as the psychoanalysts say, and becomes a partial support for the physician-drug effect (Balint), especially if the verbal wrapping of it improves the psychotherapeutic effects.

But in our times, confidence in science, the scientistic

mentality, wonder drugs, and the miracles of surgery (all coming less from true science than from science fiction or premature information) all contribute to making therapeutics play the role formerly played by *magic*. The magical action of medicine continues to work on the eternal primitive side of man, but now under the cover of science. This allows civilized people to indulge their credulity and their need for magic under rational appearances. Thus, these psychotherapeutic actions of the drug give it an efficacity independent of its pharmacodynamic reality. These actions should be researched in depth in order to diminish their dangers.

But, and this is what I am driving at, it is also a double-edged weapon and produces dangers of a special type for the patient: that of indolence, of cowardice, of *flight* in the face of one's problems and one's responsibilities. The patient requests medicines for suppressing his fatigue and its effect, for increasing his memory, for becoming more intelligent, for finding peace and joy without effort, artificially, without contributing and without undertaking his own battle against sickness, for returning to a normal state.

A patient who found his mystical *élans* a little too brief asked me if I didn't have some pills that would give birth to the feeling of divine grace!

As some women consider that the trade of the obstetrician is to bring the child into the world ("Put me to sleep and take it out"), so do patients demand of their physicians devices and recipes for *resolving through chemistry the problems of their lives*. We are not speaking here of the search for false utopias, but more simply of this search for *la vie en rose*, for euphoria, which has now become customary through the use of psychotropic drugs (resulting, for example, from the findings made during the course of a reducing treatment).

But behind this ersatz serenity and plentitude looms a more serious problem, that of the eternal human desire for the *superman.* This is not simply the artist who seeks inspiration in drugs as formerly he sought it in alcohol, coffee, or opium, or the businessman hoping to play the dynamic and powerful superman, or those modern political philosophies which want to modify man according to the needs of society. Rather, this superman—let us not be deceived—is shaped according to the Nietzschean revolt against God, the desire to install oneself in his place in order to undertake creation and to re-create it according to a particular plan.

Following this patient-medicine relationship, let us now look at the physician-medicine relationship, for it also poses its problems.

Here we should examine our consciences and make our self-criticism on the way we prescribe drugs, in order to look at the dangers which come from our way of prescribing them.

It is certain that we should consider as an aspect of fatigue, the fatigue of the physician whose life is irregular, who is overworked and burdened with responsibilities. The sacrifice of his personal and mental hygiene can have serious consequences. And Balint has put it well when he remarked that the radiologist keeps an eye on the proper working condition of his machine and the cardiologist verifies the correctness of the electrocardiographic traces, but the practitioner does not pay enough attention to the good condition of his own organism.

Another danger comes from the increasing difficulty which the physician has of keeping himself informed about new medicines. He feels overwhelmed by the evolution of the sciences, by their growing complexity. Throwing in the basket all the articles which it is impossible for him to read each morning, he feels discouraged in the face of the difficulties in keeping abreast properly and the necessity of artificially limiting himself.

But he also has a feeling of the lowering of the quality of this information. Besieged by excessive advertising, he is influenced by the mass effect of conditioning repetitions. Thus, when he writes out his prescriptions, he feels the results of the association of words, ideas, and pictures, all coming from the stock of advertising material read in the morning mail (with all the astuteness this material shows for helping our memory).

A few days ago a pharmaceutical salesman showed me some suppositories for allaying pelvic and utero-ovarian pains. The name was a chemical term, absolutely unpronounceable. To facilitate things, the drug had been called, according to the current fashion, by its initials— P.M.B.P.P. Since that did not make it much easier to remember, the salesman suggested to me, "Listen, Doctor, it is not difficult. All you have to do is to remember the suppositories *"Pour Ma Belle Pépée"* ["For My Beautiful Girlfriend"].

The physician suffers such things with even more qualms and regrets because he has the very clear impression that there has been a devalorization in the scientific worth of present-day technical medical publications. To be sure, these publications glitter with impressive, multicolored graphs, statistical charts, and an austere and serious air, all designed to reassure the physician and to render him guiltless, to give him a good conscience. But one does not have to scratch very far to discover that, beneath the surface, scientific exactness is too often precarious.

These observations are based on a few cases, gathered from disparate subjects, studied from a narrow perspective and in too short a time. This rubbish leads one to systematically doubt this literature in which it is difficult to separate the wheat from the chaff and, swamped by this inundation, one's critical spirit is weakened and one falls back on the magic of the words used. "One breaks the circuit," as it were. For example, a physician encounters a refractory case of sciatica. In prescribing a certain medicine, it is so pleasant and restful for him to think: "I am disconnecting," as if he turned off an electric switch.

The physician is also hard pressed by the thirst of patients for drugs. A dangerous therapeutic demagoguery is being created, activated by competition. An outbidding has arisen to show off the end of ends, the latest miracle drug to arrive from the U.S.A. or elsewhere.

There are also dangers arising from complaints of families and lawsuits if, following a complication, one has not prescribed massive doses of reputedly infallible drugs. This, of course, would only be self-protection, or "umbrella coverage" as they say in the army.

But let us go deeper into the motivations which push us to prescribe sometimes dangerous drugs, for an understanding of them can permit us to be less injurious. First, there is a certain perfectly valid technical curiosity. But this can also lead us to take risks and imprudent attitudes in the name of a necessary experimentation. Under this cover how many more or less unconscious feelings and impulses are much less valid.

First of all, there is pride. It seems shameful to prescribe an aspirin tablet, so one makes a prescription worthy of a great consultant. Out of self-pride, one uses a cannon to kill a fly. The need for power and domination quite often shows through under the authority (otherwise so useful) of the physician. This can go as far as a certain aggressiveness and sadism which is not the attribute only of the surgeons. As Held has said, one "hides under the chemical cover one's own aggressive counter-transferential reactions."

On the other hand, the desire to please or to attract, or the feeling of piety or of sympathy, can also lead one to prescribe dangerously.

Finally, the anxiety of the physician (he needs some, but not too much) can lead him to lose his self-control and to release the great waters of pharmacopoeia to all comers, through fear of unexpected complications or of diagnostic errors. On the contrary, if his fear concerns the toxicity of the drugs, he will prescribe sometimes ineffective doses. The danger will be one of lack. Thus this physician will join, by other ways, the too-optimistic physician who prescribes in order to gain time, while awaiting the favorable or spontaneous evolution of the disease.

This brief survey of the therapeutic indications of drugs from the standpoint of the character of physicians is useful for putting us on guard against a certain way of prescribing which depends more on our personal motivations than on the situation of the patients, the illnesses and the pharmacological action of the drugs. To discover this and to be aware of it is to make ourselves less dangerous in practice.

But, above all, as is true on the level of the patient, the drug is also for the physician a screen, a mask, a distraction which centralizes all his action. The drug is thus an *easy solution*. It becomes dangerous not by itself but because, to the degree that we depend solely on it, we pass over other important aspects of the prescription and often fail to recognize the true problems.

For example, the medicine allows us to get rid of a patient with a medicinal prescription which cuts short the consultation and saves time by making everyone content. From this fact, the installation of the *physician-patient relationship* tends to be reduced to the minimum, to disappear from the physician's sight, to be dodged.

This is not the place to develop the importance of the physician-patient relationship from the diagnostic point of view, from the knowledge of the subject and his history, and from the therapeutic point of view. But the installation of a treatment, even effective and rational, could not replace this relationship. It should no longer be considered as a luxury, a somewhat superfluous addition due to the real action of the medicine. It is not simply a moment of physician-patient contact or a sugar-coated reassurance; either it is inseparable from all the words, the acts, indeed, the very presence of the physician before his patient, or it is not.

Its revalorization is one hope for contemporary medicine; its suppression, due to blind confidence in the pharmacological effects of medicines, is a grave danger.

Moreover, the drug is prescribed to suppress a symptom, to regulate the functioning of an organ or of a system, to act on one cause or several elements of the polyetilogy of the trouble; yet however complete and intricate be our medicinal prescription, it deals only with a partial aspect of the patient and of the illness.

Certainly, we augment our prescription with advice concerning diet, hygiene, and rest, but we often act as if we were reconciled to the fact that certain problems are beyond us. The medicines we serve then give us a good conscience. But having done this, to a certain degree we avoid considering the patient in his somatic and psychic totality, in his environment, his situation, his past, his hopes, and his problems of life. We deal with an illness separately in the history of the patient instead of attacking the deep, lasting causes at the base of his troubles.

Consequently, once a given organic manifestation is healed, our patient will have a neurosis or something else, because we have not gone to the bottom of his internal or external conflicts and because we will not have solved the question of his existential tension. The illness and the healing will have been examined under a perspective too restricted and too limited in duration. Under the cover of our partial success obtained with medicines, we often flee from the basic problems.

The danger of our therapeutic satisfaction is that of masking our *resignation* in the face of an understanding of the patient, and of limiting our action.

The idea of the "Medicine of the Person" should make the physician open to the meaning of his insufficiencies and should hinder us from resting on the apparent and transitory successes obtained by medicines.

In these critical remarks on the treatment of fatigue

and the danger of drugs, we have wanted simply to accentuate certain basic aspects discussed elsewhere, in purely technical publications.

And, on the occasion of this study on fatigue and on the problems it raises, a lovely phrase of Simone Weil comes to mind: "There are some people who hope to grasp the spirit of a sonata by dismantling the piano." Our role as physicians is certainly to repair and to harmonize the delicate and fragile instrument that is entrusted to us, so that it will function properly and give forth a correct sound. But does our role not also include the attempt to bring forth harmony from it by grasping its meaning?

# Fatigue and Rest According to the Bible

GEORGES CRESPY

The way in which the Scriptures speak of fatigue and rest cannot be understood if we do not first of all understand that the biblical languages never make our familiar distinction between *work* and *fatigue*. For example, John 4:6 presents Jesus to us, seated beside the well, *wearied* by the journey. But the same chapter has Jesus address the disciples with the following remarks: "I sent you to reap that for which you did not *labor;* others have *labored*, and you have entered into their *labor*" (vs. 38). The same verb is employed in both of these passages.

In the same way, Luke 5:5, which deals with the miraculous catch of fish, could be translated: "we toiled all night and took nothing" or "we were wearied all night . . ." Thus we learn first of all that work, unsurprisingly, involves the very act of working. But a more fruitful idea appears when we link the verb which expresses both work and fatigue to its root. The root is, in fact, the idea of "to cut," "*to sever*," and, in a wider sense, "to be in pain." The fatigue of work is its pain, for work amputates, molests, breaks. Only the lilies of the field neither "toil" nor are in pain (Matt. 6:28; Luke 12:27), because

they have no "anxiety." It is only man who is, at the same
time, the being who works, becomes tired and pained,
the *anxious being*.

Is this to say that the Bible does not know our modern
distinction between physiological fatigue and nervous or
existential fatigue (to be tired *of living* and by life)? A
text, of great importance for our purposes, should pro-
vide us with a first step in answering this question, and
will later lead us to a more profound reflection. We find,
in Matthew's Gospel (11:28-30), a statement by Jesus,
the original context of which we are unfortunately igno-
rant (although the context in which the Evangelist
places it is itself full of interest). We will quote it in its
most customary translation, and will then give a rough
analysis of its meaning:

"Come to me, all who labor and are heavy laden, and
I will give you rest. Take my yoke upon you, and learn
from me; for I am gentle and lowly in heart, and you will
find rest for your souls. For my yoke is easy, and my
burden is light."

According to what we have previously said, it should
not be at all surprising that "labor" could also be translated "fatigued."* It is possible, without doing violence
to the text, to propose: "You who are *fatigued by dint of
working*." But that which is translated by "heavy laden"
does not stand by itself. It can be understood only
through the allusion Jesus makes to the yoke. The idea
contained in this is, in fact, *to be heavy laden with a burden*. Jesus would propose the substitution of *his* yoke for
the burden which is borne by those whom he summons.

---

* Translator's note: The French version does translate it "fatigued."

Can the nature of this burden be ascertained? We can observe that after having proposed his yoke, Jesus adds: "and *learn* from me." It is clear that this "apprenticeship" is that which a disciple serves under his master, since the verb translated by "to learn" should be literally rendered by: "to be the disciples of . . ." Thus it is understood, through the very wish of Jesus to present his own teaching, that the "burden" in question is not unrelated to a *teaching* which the people addressed by Jesus himself have already received. It is a *teaching which oppresses men.*

Confirmation of this interpretation is given by the narrative which the Evangelist places immediately after the text being considered. It concerns the well-known episode of the disciples eating grain as they passed through the field on a Sabbath (Matt. 12:1-8). On this occasion, Jesus is led to say that the Son of Man is Lord of the Sabbath. It is not without reason that the Evangelist has joined these two narratives. Nor is it without reason that he has preceded the words concerning the yoke with a speech by Jesus on the false wisdom of the sages and on the revelation of truth to children (11:25-27).

The Evangelist very likely wants to communicate to us the following idea: the Pharisees and the doctors of the law have placed on man's shoulders a burden which they themselves do not bear (Matt. 23:4), for which Jesus himself was led to reproach them. This burden is oppressing. Moreover, we know what this burden consists of: it involves the multiplication of ritual and moral ordinances, of commandments and glosses on the law. Some 613 commandments have been enumerated which, during Jesus' times, were meant to be scrupulously observed,

under pain of perdition, for whoever transgressed the
smallest commandment transgressed them all. Or so the
rabbis affirmed.

As a consequence, he who trangressed the commandments became thereby "a sinner" and was cut off from
Israel. This is what happened to the "publicans" who
handled the pieces of money bearing the image of Cae-
sar. But whoever wanted to live in the community of
Israel, and to follow the teaching of its sages, was forced
by this to submit to all of the commandments, which
could only constitute for him an absolutely insupportable
burden.

Thus we can see why the question of obedience to the
law appears constantly in the Gospel narratives. Further-
more, Jesus' receptive attitude toward those who did not
observe the law (the prostitutes and "sinners") is a profound witness, as the legalists indignantly recognized,
against the conception of salvation based on obedience to
the law. Men, already fatigued by work, were further
oppressed by the religion of the law. Among them, the
oppression did not result from physical fatigue alone, nor
even from physiological misery, which is certainly considerable, but also from *the impossibility of being truly at
peace with God* through the means that had been
taught them. For it is impossible to obey all the commandments simultaneously. Jesus ironically called this to
the attention of the Pharisees by leading them to observe
that obedience to the commandment which declares as
"Corban" anything which has been set aside for the Temple brings people to sin against the duty of assisting one's
parents, a duty which is also proclaimed by the law
(Mark 7:11).

In short, the "fatigue" of the oppressed results from their not being able to succeed in establishing a harmonious relationship with God. But this deficiency in the relationship with God results in a deficiency in the relationship with oneself. The tax collector of the parable is the model of the oppressed. To be sure, his attitude contains, primarily, regret for the sin which has estranged him from God, and for this he will remain exemplary in any event. Yet there is also the confession of a failure to please God through the means which the Pharisee thought quite easy to follow (as it concerned him). This is confirmed by his standing apart from the Pharisee. The tax collector is miserable from being what he is. So it was necessary for Jesus to reveal to us that this miserableness of being is the very condition of justification: the tax collector rather than the Pharisee "went down to his house justified" (Luke 18:9-14).

Perhaps some will think that there must be some relation between this miserableness of being and the fact that man is a sinner, as there is an evident relation, according to Genesis 3, between the Fall and the fatigue of work. It is quite true that *sin oppresses* and that the knowledge of sin fatigues with a deadly fatigue (cf. Psalm 38:6-7, even though this text is difficult to interpret). But it is also necessary to observe that, in the context of our text, oppression does not come from sin, but from the remedy proposed to fight against sin and to become agreeable to God. *The remedy is worse than the evil* and is at the origin of fatigue through oppression.

Let us make a prudent generalization. In the matter of sin, the remedies that we sometimes invent are always worse than the evil. If we mean by sin a fundamental disharmony in the relationship to God which provokes a fundamental disharmony in the relationship with the neighbor, is it not clear that everything we can invent to remedy this disharmony eventually encloses us in a condition worse than the sheer sinful condition? More precisely, our contrivances in this area belong to the very economy of sin and to its logic, for there is no sheer sinful condition. The New Testament presents to us, in the law, the power which can make sin abound, but we have also discovered other types of conduct as injurious, in the final analysis, as legalism and which obviously have the same effect.

For example, we have invented *overflowing activity, systematic amusement* (without forgetting the "rest of the warrior," which we have not had to invent). To be sure, these conducts do not have the same intrinsic value. They have only, in certain respects, the same *function*. They aid us in fleeing from the established fact, toward which we would be led if we could remain alone before ourselves and know ourselves such as we are, i.e., of a fundamental disharmony in the center of our existence.

This is because we do not succeed in accepting ourselves, for want of being unable to accept our condition before God, because we indulge ourselves in these activities. Moreover, they are equivocal and it is their equivocalness which make them intolerable. In fact, between a normal activity and a dissolute activity, there is, at first sight, only a difference of *degree*. This is why one can slip from one to the other without recognizing that they are not of the same *nature*.

Individual variations are added to the variations which proceed from the special nature of the works that we carry out, all the more so because no *norm* of activity can be supplied. We pass from the fatigue resulting from the pain of work to the fatigue resulting from the "yoke" which we have put on our shoulders without even taking account of it. We become prisoners of pathologic conducts at the very moment where we think that we are still able to place ourselves in a hygiene of existence regulated by work. And all pretexts become good in order to persevere in an existential error which presents all the aspects of a therapeutic.

The same is true for recreation. It is impossible to make a person believe that his mania for bridge, for example, covers only a flight. In reality, we are just as "heavy laden," but since our "burdens" do not have a specific religious content (there are no faddists of worship or biblical study who push their mania to the point of fatigue), they do not appear as "burdens."

This is why, earlier, I proposed a prudent generalization. The prudence was not dictated by the difficulty of understanding the general meaning of certain of our conducts, but rather by the difficulty of discerning the hidden *religious meaning* of conducts which are resolutely secular.

In fact, legalism is frankly an effort to remedy the sinful condition by attempting to be acceptable to God. The oppression which it provokes is still a way of being in relationship with God. Our own oppressions, according to the norms of a radically secularized thought, at first sight no longer have the same contents. But who does not see that the rich man whose overflowing activity refills the storehouses, or the prodigal son who dissipates his wealth in debauchery, already represent in the Gos-

pels radically secularized types, whose conducts, moreover, could be clarified only theologically. Both flee their
true destiny, in a nonlegalist manner, and both illustrate
"fatiguing" attitudes to which, doubtless, the call of Jesus is also addressed: "Come to me, all who labor and
are heavy laden . . ." It is true that the polemical point
against wealth risks veiling this situation, since on the
whole, he who chose to alienate himself in debauchery
repented, whereas the rich man was only *warned* of the
necessity of repenting.

But it will suffice for our purposes that the fatigue resulting from the "burden" weighing on our shoulders is
never unrelated to the fact that we work to construct
veritable systems of defense against the existential disharmony which Scripture calls sin. It is also true that
our situation is different from that of Jesus' listeners, in
the sense that they *suffered* from a system imposed on
them by sociological and cultural pressures, whereas we
enjoy a relatively greater freedom, due to the very secu-
larization of our mentality.

One point remains concerning fatigue-burden. We
have seen that the Pharisees load men down with burdens which they themselves do not bear. They do not
participate in the oppression which they provoke. This is
because they have found a means of escape in *judgment*,
as the parable of the Pharisees and the publican, once
again, shows us. The Pharisee is in a condition of relative
*repose*, that is, of peace with God (we know that this is
a peace within alienation, but he does not realize this) in
exact proportion to the extent to which he can compare
his "existential success" with the failure of the publican.
From this we learn that fatigue is also of the order of in-

terhuman relationships. We know that Elijah, exhausted by the combat carried on against his enemies, came to say of it: "It is enough; now, O LORD, take away my life" (1 Kings 19:4), and we know that God gave him rest by restoring him, so great is God's pity for the fatigue of his servants. And we know also that St. Paul, "hard pressed between the two," felt in his turn the desire "to depart and be with Christ" (Phil. 1:23). God's service fatigues, through the confrontation of men which it imposes. Moreover, such service involves a fatigue without "complexes." But we are acquainted with the ease with which we render others responsible for our fatigues, and the type of shame that we show when we rest while others work. Thus it is not surprising that fatigue is contagious and equally contagious are the patterns of behavior leading to fatigue. This leads us to fear that a pastor can never feel that he is normal unless he is "overworked." But this all belongs to a psychology of fatigue, and we must limit ourselves to indicating a possible theological basis for such a psychology, by recalling that the oppression from which we suffer is never unrelated to the fact that we always feel that we have overcome by ourselves the anxiety which results from our disharmonious condition, before men and before God. Moreover, we will not yet leave this order of reflection, seeking now to understand what Jesus tells us about rest.

"I will give you rest." Some of the English versions have: "I will refresh you," and the *Bible of Jerusalem* (French) has: "I will lighten your load." These translations come closer to the grammatical form of the Greek: "I will rest you." This form is impossible in French (and English), where the verb "to rest" ceases to be reflexive only when it designates the (eternal) rest of the dead (Here rests . . . !). It signifies that *we rest* ourselves, whereas in the biblical languages it is *God* who gives *us* rest. In fact, despite the grammar, rest is not a thing which we would possess and which we could communicate to ourselves. *God is our rest.* In other words, rest has a source outside of ourselves.

Moreover, this is why the biblical idea of rest does not cover only the idea of a suspension of activity (in this case the reflexive form would be suitable), but also the idea of a *repairing* and *regeneration.* The idea of *refreshing* renders it all the better because the image of the oasis in the desert has profound echoes in the Old Testament. For the nomad, rest is linked with the abundance of food, with shade, and especially with water. Thus it is not surprising that the prophetic preaching announced the coming Kingdom in a series of images evocative of flowing waters and succulent food (Isa. 41:18; 43:20; Joel 3:18, etc.). These agrarian and rustic images express a nomadic sensibility. As has often been observed, humanity has fallen from a *garden*, a garden where the Creator deigned to walk in the cool of the evening. Consequently, it is not astonishing that rest be linked to *paradise*, as fatigue is sometimes linked to the wandering in the desert. To the people who left Egypt and crossed the desert, it was a type of garden that was promised, a garden whose fruits were enormous and juicy.

We can also observe, by a condensation of the images frequently utilized in Hebrew thought, that the land of Canaan, the Kingdom of God, as well as all the renewals of the covenant during the periods of exile, are closely tied to rest, by means of the images of the garden. In particular, the past, the entry into the Promised Land, and the future, the Kingdom of God, are compressed into a single event, whose general sense expresses *refreshment*.

When Jesus said, "I will rest you," he was thus announcing that the messianic times had come. Indeed, at the very moment when God creates, according to the prophecy of Isaiah (65:17 ff.), "new heavens and a new earth," a solemn promise is made that the people will be glad, that human beings will live at least a hundred years, but also that man's work will no longer be despoiled: "they shall plant vineyards and eat their fruit. They shall not build and another inhabit," etc. The prophet adds: "They shall not labor in vain." In other words, rest will not be the suspension of work, but the untroubled fructification of work. The sign of the Kingdom is not the extinction of activity, but the end of the wear and tear brought on by activity. That is the rest which God provides for his people. We can thus understand how Jesus' words accord with what has been said earlier concerning the fatigue of work. Jesus, the Messiah, opens the times of a work without fatigue.

But this age is also a time of reconciliation. It is an age without "burden." This is what Jesus points to in his allusion to his yoke and to his teaching. Jesus substitutes the easy *yoke* of his teaching for the burden of the instruction of the Pharisees and lawyers. To be sure, at first sight, the image of a yoke does not exactly evoke the idea of rest. However, it must be noted that the word we have translated as "easy" is the translation, in the Greek version of the Old Testament, of an adjective

with which we are well acquainted, since we encounter
it as early as the first chapter of Genesis. When it tells
that all that which God had made was "good," the Hebrew term thus rendered is the very one which the
Greek Old Testament translates by the word which we
find in our text. Thus, without forcing the text, we could
easily read: "my yoke is *good*." But it would remain to
point out that this adjective in no wise refers to a moral
value. When a creation is "good" for God, it means that it
is conformed *to the end* which the Creator had assigned
to it. Thus the yoke of Christ is conformed to the end
pursued by Jesus, suited to serve this end. Evidently, the
"light burden" becomes, if we keep close to the text, the
"burden easy to carry," the original meaning of the adjective being: "brisk," "agile." Modified by these consid-
erations, the image of the yoke becomes less oppressive.

In Israel, the law was long considered as a yoke (Jer.
2:20; 5:5; Hos. 11:4; Lam. 3:27). And Paul specified that
the law was the yoke under which Christians should not
place themselves again at any price (Acts 15:10; Gal. 5:
1). In proposing *his* yoke, easy and light, Christ set his
teaching over against that of the doctors of the law. But
what is the content of this teaching? The Gospel tells us.
It consists of the good news that the times are accomplished and that it is now necessary to live in the hope
and promise of the Kingdom of God.

Even more, Jesus specified that this Kingdom is for the
"humble," for those who have been called "the people of
the Beatitudes." To this people, he proclaimed that ser-
vitude to the law is finished, that these new times have
begun in which he who believes will be saved. This
teaching is not exercised in the severity of an inflexible

law, but in the "gentleness" and "lowliness of heart" of Jesus. This is why we find in him "rest for the soul."

We touch here on an idea which has provoked great misunderstandings. By "rest for the soul," in fact, a whole quietist tradition means an escape from activity. This does not seem to be the meaning indicated by the Gospel text. The "rest for the soul" refers to the end of its anxieties, whereas the restless soul wonders how to be acceptable to God. Jesus proclaims to the tormented soul that *the time of peace has come,* because God has resolved to be reconciled to men, not because of their obedience to the law, but by reason of their availability for the good news of the Kingdom. Peace does not exclude activity. On the contrary, the Lord acts, and it is necessary to act quickly, before the night comes. But this activity is not feverishly turned toward a salvation to be gained; it is polarized by a salvation heralded and already present.

We can now understand more fully the biblical meaning of rest. *Rest is in relation to the Kingdom of God.*

We could already have an inkling of this through the theme of rest par excellence, the theme of the Sabbath found throughout Scripture. Our conclusion can only be reinforced by the episode of the disciples eating the ears of grain on the Sabbath, that has been very opportunely —and not unintentionally, in my opinion—placed by the Evangelist following the statements on which we have already commented. The most obvious sign that the Kingdom of God is come is that the Sabbath rediscovers all its *liberty,* through the mastery exercised over it by the Son of Man. A proof that the "yoke" of Christ is easy and light is indeed given to us in the fact that the disciples are no longer bound by the discipline of the Sabbath. They were hungry, they could eat, and, in order to eat, they could "work" on the Sabbath. This was not because they had obtained for themselves a previously dormant liberty, but because their master is Lord of the Sabbath. The Sabbath was not just one occasion among others through which Jesus manifested his kingship. It was the manifestation par excellence of this kingship. This is already alluded to in the Gospel accounts where the legalists are scandalized by Jesus' attitude toward the Sabbath. The Sabbath is a critical place for the proclamation of the rule of God. This derives from its very nature. In order to understand this point, it will be necessary to devote some time to a recalling of the meaning of the Sabbath.

The Old Testament, of course, contains several narratives concerning the institution of the Sabbath. It is important to note that the two "decalogues" which tradition has left to us do not give the same reasons for the observing of this day of rest. (Let us remember that "Sabbath" comes from a verb meaning "to cease from labor.") According to Exodus 20:11, the Sabbath should be observed, "for in six days the LORD made heaven and earth, the sea, and all that is in them, and rested the seventh day; therefore the LORD blessed the sabbath day and hallowed it." According to Deuteronomy 5:15, "You shall remember that you were a servant in the land of Egypt, and the LORD your God brought you out thence with a mighty hand and an outstretched arm; therefore the LORD your God commanded you to keep the sabbath day."

In short, in the first case, the Sabbath refers to the *rest* of God, while in the second case, it celebrates his liberating *activity*. Despite appearances, these two explanations are complementary. In effect, the rest of God in no way indicates the absence of God in the world, but a new mode of his presence. God has created and now, remaining over against his creation, he assumes with it, through man, a *relationship* to which the whole Bible is to render witness. But, in this relationship, he does not cease acting. The Sabbath, then, does not evoke divine immobility, and even less the fatigue of the Creator (innumerable texts show that God did not tire of loving his creature and of maintaining and reforming him). Rather, the Sabbath evokes the joy that proves God to be *with* his creation. As Karl Barth has rightly remarked, the "first" Sabbath is related to the perfection of the creation. It is when God said, "It is good" (we have seen that this should be translated, "It conforms to what I willed") that the Sabbath can appear. Yet God is not less present in the world in the Sabbath than in the six days of creation. The presence would be manifested precisely in the liberating action of God at the time of the Exodus. In freeing his people, God gives himself to it once again, in a new relationship, inaugurated by the liberating act. In the first case, the Sabbath reminds us that we inhabit a world which God has *willed* and which he loves. In the second case, it reminds us that we are liberated by the same God. Its original meanings, far from being opposed, overlap. This is why the Sabbath can be lived only as *adoration*, for the blessing of the creation and for the liberty which we receive from God.

It remains, then, to understand how that which is the festival of liberty could become the worst of slaveries.

The perversion of the Sabbath is many times alluded to by Scripture. Ezekiel, especially, in the vision of history that he proposes to us, refers to the "great profanation" of the Sabbath committed by the people, even before the entrance into Canaan (Ezek. 20:12 ff.).

For him, it was evident that the children of Israel had profaned the Sabbath, because "their heart went after their idols" (20:16). It was idolatry which was responsible for the scorning of the Sabbath. God was too far away; the people longed for Egypt; freedom was too trying for a people accustomed to slavery. At the confluence of these reasons appeared idolatry, which made God nearer and more available. "Up, make us gods, who shall go before us," the Hebrews said to Aaron (Exod. 32:1). Since such a god obviously cannot present the characteristics of a creator and a liberator, the worship given to it could never rediscover the inspiration of a sabbatarian worship, and the Sabbath itself would become a type of "sacrament of idolatry." Because it cannot be consecrated to God the Creator and Liberator, it is consecrated to secret idolatries. But in this consecration, it is corrupted.

Another corruption, of opposite nature, appears in the Scripture. In sum, idolatry is by essence the perversion of faith in the *Creator*, since it consists of the elevation of a creation of man to the rank of creator, as Isaiah ironically pointed out. The inverse error of the Pharisees and legalists was to have forgotten that God is the *Liberator*. They understood God's rest not as liberating activity but as a complete suspension of activity. This is why they multiplied the prohibitions relating to the Sabbath, constituting in this way the *yoke*, the *burden* which men must bear.

A strange fate for the Sabbath. Consecrated to God the Creator and Liberator, it became corrupted either in ignorance of the Creator or in ignorance of the Liberator. In the first case, it is effaced, judged useless, while man erects his own creations on a level with creative realities. He expects work or recreation (which is, in all ways, his own work) to exercise a regenerative power, impossible in any case. He thinks to give *himself* rest because he has invented something to fill up his rest.

In the second case, the Sabbath becomes the worst of slaveries. Forgetting that the Creator is also the Liberator, man turns the observance of the Sabbath into the occasion for a multiplication of the servitudes of the week. This is done either by taking advantage of Sunday to catch up on things not done during the week, or by enclosing the Sunday rest in such a great variety of "taboos" that the day of liberty is turned into the day of deadly boredom.

In any case, Jesus intended to display a perverted Sabbath (one perverted primarily, though not uniquely, according to the second mode), and confronting this Sabbath, he wanted to recall, through his own conduct, the true meaning, lost and forgotten, of the Sabbath. The Gospel texts relative to the thought of Jesus on the Sabbath are so abundant that we cannot cite them all. Rather, we will choose a somewhat unusual theme on which to center our reflections. According to John's Gospel (5:1-18), at the pool of Bethzatha, a man sick for thirty years is healed on the Sabbath. Upset by the event, Jesus' adversaries followed him and pressed him with questions. They were indignant, as usual, because he had healed on the Sabbath. Jesus' response to them is very illuminating for us: "My Father is working still, and

I am working." The Evangelist notes profoundly: "This was why the Jews sought all the more to kill him, because he not only broke the sabbath but also called God his Father, making himself equal with God" (vss. 17-18).

Thus Jesus' own words confirm our previous assertion that God does not cease to act. Truly, "he who keeps Israel will neither slumber nor sleep" (Ps. 121:4). But Jesus' declaration, "I am working," which is meant to justify his healing activity, takes on new meaning because the act which it justifies takes place precisely on the Sabbath. Why this day and not another? Several commentators have remarked that the majority of healings reported by the Evangelists take place on the Sabbath. Is this only a series of chance circumstances?

Quite the contrary, we must grasp the relationship between the act of healing and the Sabbath. Jesus did not heal simply to manifest his authority, his "power," but above all, to attest that the Kingdom of God is present. Yet why attest this especially on the Sabbath? Is it not because the Sabbath has in itself some relationship to the Kingdom of God? We are led to believe this because Jesus quite frequently chose the Sabbath to proclaim his own messiahship. Thus, at the beginning of his ministry, it was during the Sabbath preaching, in the synagogue worship service, that Jesus applied to himself Isaiah's prophecy concerning the Anointed One of the Lord. And it was the following Saturday that, teaching "with authority," he healed a demoniac (Luke 4:16-37 and parallels).

In the same way, the declaration reported by John ("My Father is working, and I am working") can be understood only in the light of messianic activity. The violation of the Sabbath for which Jesus was reproached is in direct relation to his pretension of proclaiming himself as the Son of God, and as the Evangelist says, of "making himself equal with God." The Sabbath is the unexcelled day for revealing the nearness of the Kingdom of God.

But, at the same time, the Sabbath recovers its meaning, its original double significance. It is the sign of God's presence in the world and of an active, *transforming* presence whose purpose becomes evident. God is involved in establishing his reign and in making known, in the Sabbath, the very reality of his reign. At that time all the Old Testament images concerning *rest* take their place. In effect, in the prophetic preaching the reign of God *is rest for man.* It is the end of all his physiological and mental miseries. It is the end of the alienation of work, and, let us note in passing, it is also the rest of the entire creation, which does not know the Sabbath (Gen. 8:22).

Such is the situation when Jesus speaks. He argues, in short, for a return to the Sabbath that God has willed, and he gives new meanings to this Sabbath through his declarations concerning his own messiahship and the presence of the Kingdom of God.

Was this situation changed when the Christian church substituted Sunday for Saturday? On the contrary, this substitution goes beyond the theological content of the Sabbath. Sunday incorporates all the meanings of the Sabbath and adds to them, in that the resurrection of Jesus Christ actualizes and registers in events the divine activity. The resurrection of Jesus Christ is the *act* par excellence by which God declares his wish to make all things new, in overcoming death itself. The church was not wrong in choosing the day of the Lord's resurrection as its weekly day of rest.

But, through this substitution the church has given us something to understand profoundly—*rest itself*. In fact, rest becomes a promise of resurrection and of life, a promise of a new order, where man will no longer be oppressed. It is not only the suspension of activity, but rather, the assuming of an objective perspective over against our activities, in order to clarify them by the light of the resurrection. Sunday rest is a foretaste of the world to come.

Is this to say that the world to come will annul the world which is? This is an important question, for it requires an *ethic of rest*, and consequently, an *ethic of activity*.

Activity and rest ordinarily belong to the *human ethos*. Human life is created from the expenditure-recovery rhythm, as is animal life. But the difference between the human ethos and the animal ethos, in this regard, is that rest, in the animal, is not solely the result of the need for recovery, but proceeds also from the absence of an intellectual life. The animal sleeps because he cannot think. Man sleeps when he decides to think no longer. In other words, the work-rest rhythm is not purely natural in man; it also follows the cultural nature of man. Man is the being capable of deciding, up to a point, that he will not rest, just as he can decide to slow down certain physiological activities voluntarily, for example, by fasting. This power he commands profoundly transforms his "natural" condition. Thus "naturism" for example, is only hidden "culturalism."

But, if this is the case, how does man arrange his activity or his rest? Let us point out that most frequently he does not, properly speaking, make arrangements in the matter. He submits to a law which is imposed on him, he believes, by his environment. He rests because it is necessary to rest; he works because it is necessary to work. A certain discipline is imposed on him from outside. It comes from afar, since weekly rest, for example, seems to have made its appearance well before the institution of the Sabbath (because the cycle of festivals in ancient civilizations was established soon after the origins of these civilizations). But this discipline, because it is a compromise between the natural and the social, varies as the "social" varies. For example, paid vacations partake of our *ethos* and can hardly vary except in the direction of elongation. The Middle Ages did not know paid vacations. True, they knew more than one hundred days off (including Sundays), at times of festivals ordained by the church.

But, in any event, it is a certain relationship between economic production, the organization of life, and religious constraint which has regulated man's rest up to now, and will undoubtedly also regulate it in the future. Nevertheless, the religious component loses more and more of its importance. As with everything else, rest is becoming secularized. It has even been necessary to institute, in some places, weekday worship services for people obliged to work on Sunday.

The effect of this evolution is especially serious in that both rest and activity are less and less related to a world of values which refer man to Something beyond his empirical existence. We are more and more, it seems, in a full-blown empiricism. We have an *ethos* of rest; we no longer have an *ethic* of rest. This civilization of leisure into which we have entered must know new developments, and in light of this, we are in danger of soon finding ourselves in the presence of *frameworks* of rest which are larger and larger but which are also more and more empty. More precisely, we are in danger of finding in the future that a part of the population (the technicians, for example) will rest less and less, while another part of the population will rest more and more. But neither the over-activity of some nor the leisure of the others will have the least ethical meaning.

It seems to me, as a consequence, that the task of Christians is to call to mind that our rest as well as our work refers us to One beyond ourselves. Such is the real importance of preaching on the subject of the Sabbath. Let us note that this does not involve a regulating of the Christian Sunday according to a ready-made model, but of giving to this Sunday its prophetic meaning as the period when man is informed again and again that he is not alone, but that a love which prepares for him a new world, envelopes him and honors his activity. It would obviously be necessary, to make this perfectly clear, to reflect on the meaning of man's *work*, but this is not our present purpose.

Certain manuscripts of the Gospel of Luke have preserved a narrative which is not usually included in our modern versions of the Bible. This passage, which comes after Luke 6:5, is as follows: "The same day, seeing someone working on the Sabbath, [Jesus] said to him, 'O man, if you know what you do, you are happy, but if you do not know, you are evil and a transgressor of the Law.'"

"If you know what you do, you are happy." If, in full understanding, you have decided that the Sabbath was for you, you are happy. The commentators add, rightly, that Jesus evidently alludes to his own idea of the Sabbath, viz., the freedom which is introduced into the Sabbath when it is understood that the Sabbath is given to man in order that he might live in the world of the Kingdom of God. For my part, I think that it is wonderful how the Lord has called attention to reflection and to being aware, thereby stressing that anything is preferable to being unaware. But does the man of today know what he does? And how will he learn it if we do not tell him?